D0122106

TITLES AVAILABLE FROM LAGOON BOOKS:

<u>MIND BENDING PUZZLE BOOKS</u>

MIND-BENDING LATERAL THINKING PUZZLES	(ISBN 1899712062)
MORE MIND-BENDING LATERAL THINKING PUZZLES (VOL II)	(ISBN 1899712194)
MIND-BENDING CONUNDRUMS & PUZZLES	(ISBN 1899712038)
MIND-BENDING CLASSIC LOGIC PUZZLES	(ISBN 1899712186)
MIND-BENDING CLASSIC WORD PUZZLES	(ISBN 1899712054)
MIND-BENDING CROSSWORD PUZZLES	(ISBN 1899712399)

FANTASTIC OPTICAL ILLUSIONS & PUZZLES	(ISBN 1899712402)
WHERE IN THE WORLD AM I? - MYSTERY GEOGRAPHY PUZZLES	(ISBN 1899712410)
AFTER DINNER GAMES	(ISBN 1899712429)
MIND-BOGGLERS	(ISBN 1899712445)
PUB TRIVIA QUIZ	(ISBN 189971250X)
60 SECOND MURDER PUZZLES	(ISBN 1899712453)

<u>MYSTERY PUZZLE BOOKS</u>

DEATH AFTER DINNER	(ISBN 1899712461)
MURDER ON THE RIVIERA EXPRESS	(ISBN 189971247X)
MURDER IN MANHATTAN	(ISBN 1899712488)
MURDER AT THRIPPLETON HALL	(ISBN 1899712496)

50 OF THE FINEST DRINKING GAMES	(ISBN 1899712178)

Books can be ordered from bookshops by quoting the above ISBN numbers.
Some titles may not be available in all countries. All titles are available in the UK.

MURDER
ON THE
RIVIERA EXPRESS

A *Mystery* PUZZLE BOOK

LAGOON
BOOKS

YOU ARE THE DETECTIVE!

Series Editor: Simon Melhuish
Editor: Heather Dickson
Author: Nick Hoare
Page design and layout: Gary Sherwood & Gary Inwood Studios
Cover design, & original illustrations in the style of Gibson:
Gary Sherwood

Published by:
LAGOON BOOKS
PO BOX 311, KT2 5QW, UK

ISBN: 189971247X

Printed in Singapore

INTRODUCTION

You are a police constable. You enjoy your job and have arrested more petty thieves and hardened criminals than any of your colleagues but you are itching for promotion. It was your childhood dream to become a private investigator and you are desperate to join the rank of detective and become one of the favoured few in the local murder squad. With a lot of hard work you should be able to achieve your goal within the next five years.

Then out-of-the-blue, a file hits your desk which could completely change your fortune. It has been sent to you by the police in the south of France. The famous English novelist Cornelius Vernon has been found murdered on the luxurious Riviera Express. The local police are more used to dealing with stolen bicycles and lost passports than handling a high-profile murder investigation so your former pen-pal Jacques Perciflage has stepped into the breach. After gathering a whole dossier of evidence, Jacques is still baffled. As the press and the authorities are desperate to find the killer, he has turned to you, his old friend and English counterpart, for help.

At last your chance to secure an early promotion and outshine your Gallic rival, whose meteoric rise through the ranks has left you astounded and more than a little envious. All the information you need to catch the murderer is in this file. All you need to do is come up with a solution after reading the press cuttings, reports and transcripts of interviews contained in the dossier.

The files have been translated into English, so there's no excuse.....

Index

USEFUL TIPS

- All the information *except the actual interviews with the six suspects* is 100% accurate. Whether or not it is relevant, or particularly helpful, to your detective work is another matter altogether.
- Inspector Perciflage has interviewed all the other passengers and cabin staff who were travelling on the Riviera Express and has correctly discounted them as murder suspects.
- The murderer is not necessarily the only person who is lying. Other suspects may have done things which they do not want to admit, so they might lie to cover their actions.
- The murderer acted alone. Other suspects may well have had motives for killing the deceased, or may well point the finger at some one they think did it, but no one except the murderer and hopefully yourself, by the time you have read the book, know who is guilty.
- Your friend Inspector Perciflage is fallible. If not, he wouldn't need your help. Throughout the book there are times when he will assess the new developments. He has so far failed to solve the case, so you are advised to take your own notes while you read the book.

Remember, catching the murderer could land you with the promotion of your dreams.

Good luck!

MARSEILLES MATIN

14th August 1935

EMINENT WRITER SHOT DEAD ON RIVIERA EXPRESS

By Geraldine LeFevre

POPULAR novelist and man of letters Cornelius Vernon has been found dead in his sleeper car on the Riviera Express. He is believed to have died from a gunshot wound to the temple.

Mr Vernon, aged 34, had been holidaying on the Côte d'Azur with his wife, society hostess and patron of the arts Maude Malmaison Vernon, and a number of friends at their villa on Cap Ferrat.

The party was travelling to Marseilles when Mr Vernon's body was discovered by his wife, after the train left Chargot station at around 00.05 hours this morning. Vernon of Mayfair, London, rose to fame and fortune after his first novel "Requiem For The Walking Wounded" met with world-wide acclaim and rose to the top of the best seller list on both sides of the Atlantic.

He had been in France for some time, putting the finishing touches to his second novel.

Details of the incident are as yet unclear but local police are believed to be treating it as murder.

At the time of going to press, no one has been apprehended but the party of six travelling with the deceased have all been detained for questioning.

Scene of Crime Report

Date: 14th August 1935.

Offence: Murder.

Victim: Cornelius Cecil Vernon, male, 34 years.

Perpetrator: Unknown.

Location: Wagon Lit D, Riviera Express Chargot Station.

Description:
Body located in compartment 4. Found lying half on the floor, half on the seat. No apparent sign of struggle. A 0.22 calibre two-shot antique derringer found on floor of compartment. One round missing from the breech. Tests revealed weapon had been fired recently.

Cause of Death:
Gunshot wound to the head. Extensive damage suggests death was instantaneous.

First to Scene: Maude Malmaison Vernon

Time: 00:05hrs

Possible Suspects:

Maude Malmaison Vernon: (F) 32.
Dual French & British nationality. Wife
of the deceased. No criminal record.

Richard Steels: (M) Aged 43.
British citizen. Profession: writer.
Friend of the deceased. Numerous
offences, mainly for being drunk &
disorderly. Charges for malicious wounding
of Patrice Momo, also a writer, dropped,
after wounded party insisted it was part
of a gentleman's agreement.

Mary-Beth Simpson: (F) 38.
US citizen. Profession: journalist.
Deceased's biographer. No criminal record,
but numerous civil actions against her
for libel and slander (including suits
brought against her by French citizens).

Brandon Simpson: (M) 48.
US citizen. Profession: film producer.
Husband of the above. One conviction for
grievous bodily harm, plus two for
carrying an unlicensed firearm.

Vladimir Kielov: (M) 52.
Former Russian citizen, seeking asylum in
France. Claims passport was confiscated
by Soviet authorities. No access to any
records.

Lucinda Compton: (F) 25.
British citizen. Friend of the deceased.
No previous convictions.

Officer on Scene: Inspector Jacques
                      Perciflage

PLAN OF RIVIERA EXPRESS

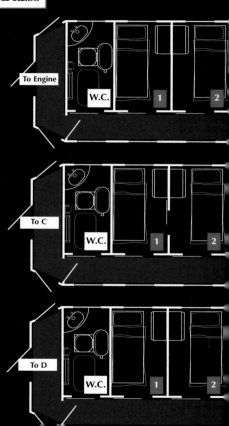

Car A
1. Richard Steels
2. Empty
3. Empty
4. Empty

All berths convert
into seating

Car D
1. Brandon Simpson
2. Mary-Beth Simpson
3. Maude M. Vernon
4. Cornelius Vernon

All berths convert
into seating

Car E
1. Lucinda Compton
2. Vladimir Kielov
3. Empty
4. Staff Room

All berths convert
into seating

To Engine

To C

To D

W.C.

1

2

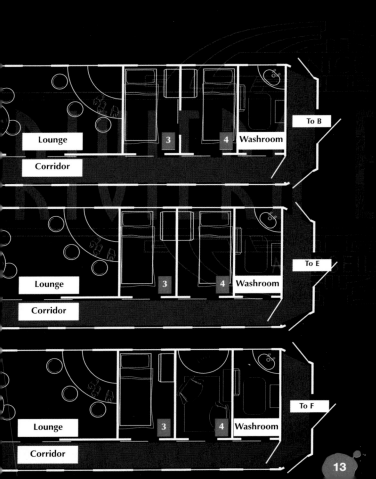

Lounge

Corridor

3

4 Washroom

To B

Lounge

Corridor

3

4 Washroom

To E

Lounge

Corridor

3

4 Washroom

To F

Maude Malmaison Vernon
Age: 32.

Heiress to an immense industrial fortune, Maude married
Vernon three years ago, much to the displeasure of her
family, who would have preferred her to wed any one of
the long line of eligible aristocrats, diplomats and men of
importance who were infatuated with her. Famed as a
patron of the arts, she met him just after his first book of
short stories was published, and supported him emotionally
and financially during the writing of his first novel. Seen by
many as "the power behind the throne",
she both encouraged him and
orchestrated the unprecedented
success of that book by tirelessly
wining and dining critics, publishers
and society writers. The ensuing
"Vernon-mania" caused them to
spend a lot of time apart, and
the month on Cap Ferrat was
the first time they had spent
together for nearly a year.

A Riviera Express hand towel, with three small holes and a number of scorch marks and powder traces, was found in the bin of Maude Malmaison Vernon's compartment.

Richard Steels
Age: 43.

Also a writer, Steels' first novel, "The Silenced Roar Of Betrayal", appeared in 1924, and documented the disillusionment and despair of a young man returning from the war. It was an enormous success, and swept Steels from obscurity to the public eye in a matter of weeks. Failing to ever quite match the success of his debut, he has produced a succession of novels to an increasingly muted critical response. Sharing similar themes and subject matter, Cornelius Vernon was feted as "the new Richard Steels", and after a magazine eventually asked Steels to interview Vernon about his imminent novel, Steels travelled down to the Villa Malmaison on Cap Ferrat. Steels has a reputation as a hard-drinking wild man, dividing his time between hunting, deep-sea fishing and brawling with other literary figures in seedy bars, occasionally fitting in the odd spot of writing.

Cornelius had a serious gambling problem. At the time of his death he had debts totalling over £150,000.

Mary-Beth Simpson
Age: 38.

Formerly a Hollywood society columnist, Mary-Beth was
one of the first people in the USA to be approached by
Maude Malmaison Vernon to publicise her husband and his
novel. Having made Vernon the toast of firstly West Coast
society, and then of the whole country, Mary-Beth saw her
chance to become more than just a Tinseltown
sleazehound, and made herself Vernon's biographer.
Travelling everywhere with him, hanging on
his every word, she is determined to capture
"the essence of one of the most important
minds of the twentieth century", despite
the fact that he has only published
one novel (albeit an enormous
best-seller world-wide)
and a handful of short
stories. She has been the
butt of many cruel jokes in
highbrow literary circles,
while her former colleagues in the
society columns have closed ranks
against her desire to leave
them behind, and some quite
salty rumours have been aired
in the less salubrious journals.

Lucinda Compton was expelled from an expensive boarding school for assaulting another girl. It was rumoured her victim had copied one of her poems and had then won a school poetry competition with it.

Brandon Simpson
Age: 48.

Mary-Beth's husband, who is ostensibly using her sojourn on
the Riviera as a good excuse for a European vacation.
Simpson is one of a new breed of film producers who have
risen to the top on the back of "the talkies". While his first
films were enormously successful, his last two bombed, losing
the studio a lot of money and making his position within
Hollywood look extremely shaky. He is desperately looking
for a film that would be sure-fire, thus shoring up his rather
precarious reputation. Before leaving
for the south of France, he promised
superiors that he would return with
a project that would make cinema
history; more cynical voices within
the industry would say that it was
the other way round, with his
superiors telling him not to
bother coming back until he'd
found something to make
that people would pay
to see. Simpson
is not a literary
man, or a
particularly patient one,
being far too accustomed to getting
what he wants.

On the floor of the compartment where Cornelius was found was an unsigned note, bearing the words "Meet me in the observation car at midnight" with a heart underneath.

Vladimir Kielov
Age: 52.

A recent addition to the Riviera's select band of idle rich, Count Vladimir Illych Kielov has become, within the space of one season, a popular figure in a social scene that less fortunate and wealthier people have spent years trying to gain access to. Dispossessed of his family's estate and great wealth by the Bolsheviks, Kielov lends an air of romantic aristocratic melancholy to any gathering at which he is present, and as a result, has found an un-stoppable river of invitations flowing to his door all Summer. Considered to be a great catch by legions of wealthy widows, his mourning for his lost heritage and childhood sweetheart prevent him from accepting the numerous offers of marriage. He is a keen campaigner and fund-raiser for the White Russian cause, and dreams of establishing an army with which to overthrow the "Bolshevik charlatans" who have "allowed peasants to eat from my father's table."
A gentleman of impeccable manners and behaviour, his only observed weaknesses are a tendency to frequent casinos and weeping with sorrow for the fate of Mother Russia after one vodka too many.

A calligraphy expert examining the note found with Cornelius' body said that it was definitely written by someone deliberately disguising his or her handwriting.

Lucinda Compton
Age: 25.

The daughter of wealthy academic parents, Lucinda is an
Oxford graduate who is determined to become a leading
woman of letters. Rejecting the staid life of post-graduate
studies at a British university, she has used her private
income to travel the world, meeting as many great writers
as she can, and trying to "live life to the full, as it is surely
meant to be lived." She began corresponding with writers
when she was 17, becoming quite taken with
Richard Steels, both the work and the man.
About a year ago, she switched her
allegiance to Cornelius Vernon, and,
after numerous letters, managed to
gain permission from him to spend the
Summer with the Vernons at their villa.
She has spent the time buried in her own
writing, as well as in long and intense
conversations with Vernon, as to how a
writer should live, what should be the aim
of a great novel, and so on.

A cabin-staff uniform jacket was found by the side of the tracks just outside Chargot station.

**Inspector Perciflage and
Maude Malmaison Vernon.**

*Mrs Vernon, a hand towel which had three small bullet holes
in it was found in your compartment. How did it get there?*

Mon Dieu! I do not believe it. My poor husband has been dead less
than 24 hours and already you ask me - the grieving widow - if I kill
him. How could I kill him? I was in the lounge all the night.

*I'm not accusing you of anything Mrs Vernon I'm simply
trying to find out what happened last night. Tell me about
the events leading up to your discovery of your husband's
body.*

We had all had supper in the dining car, all seven of us. It was very
pleasant to begin with, very light of heart. It was like a party, with
every one teasing Cornelius about his new book.

Teasing?

Yes, I think that is the right word. You see, all Summer, when he was
writing, he was so secretive, he told no one the subject of his novel.
Not even me. But he told everyone he would reveal all before we
got to Marseilles, so everyone was quite excited. In their own way.
Lucinda said she was sure it would be the best novel of the century.
She is so silly sometimes. Maybe she was joking. Steels was saying it
would be about a writer crushed by commercialism, because that
was what "The Hammer Falls" was about.

"The Hammer Falls"?

His second novel. He was so obsessed that "Requiem For The
Walking Wounded" was copied from his own first novel. He is such
a bitter man sometimes. I would say this to Cornelius, and he would
laugh, and say that I would never understand the British humour.
Tonight, I suppose, it was all fun. Not like the Simpsons.

What were they doing?

They take everything so seriously! This woman Mary-Beth, she is
like one of these shellfish on a rock. She is depending on Cornelius,
on my husband, to make her famous. And her husband, bouf, these

talking pictures are just a toy. They will never compete with the novel, or the poetry. These Americans, they want to buy everything. They think beauty and art have a price. Ha!

What about the Russian?

Vladimir? He is very nice about it. Of all of them, he is the nicest, because when he met Cornelius and I, he had never heard of us. He likes us, because we make fun for him. He forgets all about "the fatherland", and he has fun.

But what was he doing on the night in question?

Oh, just making jokes. And drinking, of course. He is always drinking. When we all retired to the lounge in our car, he was trying to get us all to play cards. I think the literary talk bores him after a while.

What time did you move to the lounge?

They close the dining car at ten, so we left then.

Did you all go straight to the lounge en masse?

No. The Simpsons went to their compartments first. Brandon said they had to check their immigration papers. Mary-Beth said that they'd already checked them, but then he said she was so careless she'd probably made a mistake, and that they'd have to do it together. He is a bully, so that was that. They went.

How long were they gone?

Mary-Beth was about ten minutes, because I remember the little clock chiming once for the quarter hour, the moment she came in. Brandon came in at nearly half past. Oh yes, and Vladimir, when everyone had sat down, everyone except the Simpsons, that is, he said he would go and get vodka and playing cards from his room. Everyone was so excited about the book that the last thing they wanted to do was play cards and drink vodka, but no one had the heart to stop him.

How long was he gone for?

I'm not sure. I don't know where he was sleeping, maybe the other end of the train, and we all wanted to know about the book, so we forgot about him until he reappeared with a half empty bottle and some cards. Maybe half an hour.

And did your husband tell you about the book?

Not really, no. He likes...liked games, you see. He just passed around this synopsis, which had a resumé of all the characters on it. It was a little disappointing, to be honest.

What was the response to it?

It was polite. I think everyone was very disappointed not to see the manuscript, or to be told about it in detail. Cornelius could talk so beautifully, you see. To be given just a sheet of paper was an anti-climax.

Did you keep the resumé?

No. No, I didn't. It was passed back to Cornelius. He was very fastidious about such things.

What happened then?

He passed around the resumé before eleven, because at eleven we pulled into a station. I remember this because Vladimir said that what he liked about the Riviera Express was that it was always so punctual. Then people started to drift away. I think Cornelius had burst the bubble a bit. It was the sort of game he liked to play.

Who "drifted away" first?

The Simpsons, but they didn't really drift. Brandon stood up and virtually dragged Mary-Beth out of the lounge. He looked furious. I think they have a lot of problems. After about ten minutes, Steels got up. He said he wanted to stretch his legs on terra firma while he had a chance. Several minutes later Cornelius left. He said he had to do some revisions, but I think he realised he had lost his audience, that there was no more fun to be had at our expense.

Did he return to his compartment?

I don't know. He just went into the corridor and was gone. I...I never saw him alive again.

So it was you, Lucinda and Vladimir left in the lounge?

For a minute or so. Then Vladimir said that he urgently needed to send a telegraph to "his people", and he made his apologies and left. I stayed and chatted with Lucinda for a while.

Didn't you say you thought she was a little silly?

In front of my husband and Steels, yes. By herself, she is a very intelligent young woman. Very determined. We have a lot in common. Then Mary-Beth came back in, and Lucinda looked at her watch and said she was very tired. She left, and I chatted to Mary-Beth. She seemed a little upset, but I was a little upset too, with Cornelius, so I made my excuses. Mary-Beth left, I gathered my things, and just as I was leaving the lounge Vladimir came back in and we heard this breaking glass on the platform. There was a big commotion outside, people trying to see what had happened. We rushed to the window to see too. It looked like the station clock had shattered. Vladimir said that maybe it was caused by the heat. Then the whistle blew and the train started off again.

Anything else?

Yes. Steels appeared as well, yawning, wearing this ridiculous night-shirt, like a Dickens character, with his trousers rolled up underneath.

And how long after did you find Cornelius?

About five minutes later I went into Cornelius' room, and there he was. Dead. Blood everywhere. I will never forget that moment. It was so horrible. Cornelius was a great writer. A lot of people didn't like him. Maybe he wasn't a great person, but he was a great writer. He didn't deserve this.

Maude Malmaison Vernon had always had a reputation for impulsive acts of cruelty. As a teenager she killed one of her father's horses with a shotgun. The horse had thrown her in front of a suitor.

RIVIERA

À VOTRE
SERVICE

EXPRESS

Inspector Perciflage and Richard Steels.

For how long had you known the deceased?

I only met him a couple of weeks ago. This magazine, an English magazine, wanted me to interview him, you know, one novelist to another, and I come to France a lot anyhow, so I popped down to see him at the villa. Ended up staying for a spot of holiday. Bit of fishing with the idle rich, sharpens one's critical faculties, you know. Gets the juices flowing.

I understand that there was an element of resentment or bitterness between the two of you.

No more than between me and anyone else. You don't want to believe everything you read you know. It's all written by people like me you see. A bit of rivalry between two writers makes a good story if a ship hasn't sunk for a week or two. There were one or two uncanny similarities between my work and his, but that's normal. Nothing new under the sun and all that. We got on well.

Tell me about the night in question.

It was just like any other really, except Cornelius was desperately trying to get us all worked up about his book. I'd been trying to interview him about it for a fortnight, and he hadn't given me anything worth writing down, so I wasn't really expecting him to deliver the goods. Those Yanks though seemed to be lapping up every word, as if their very lives depended on it. The girl too, was all pie-eyed about it. I don't think the Russian, or whatever he is, really knew what was going on. He just smiled and said "Cheers!" a lot. He looked completely stumped when he was handed his resumé. I don't think his reading in English is as good as he pretends.

His resumé? Were you given a copy each?

Oh yes. This was all part of the joke. Corny spends ages building up this special sneak preview of his new book, then instead of the "hour with the master" we'd all been expecting, he gives us out what he says was a summary of the new novel, but all it is is a joke.

A joke?

Yes, a well-tailored joke. What he'd done was write a synopsis of a novel that was about each of us. For a nasty moment I thought mine was a real summary, and that he'd put the boot in for the things I said about him last year. Then I glanced at Lucinda's copy, and hers was different.

What did yours say?

Oh, it was about an embittered middle-aged novelist who was convinced that a dashing young novelist had plagiarised one of his books. It was called "The Sound Of Stolen Thunder". It showed real vanity, real thoughtless arrogance, but it was amusing, and that was the point. People can forgive the sharpest insult if it makes them laugh. Except no one else was laughing, apart from Corny himself, of course. Everyone was staring in horror at their scrap of paper. Then they all checked with the person sitting next to them. Well, at least they tried to, but no one wanted anyone else to see theirs. When they had all established that they were all different, and that it was a joke, there were a couple of forced smiles, you know acknowledging the joke. It was important to do that with Cornelius; if not, the torment would go on indefinitely.

Did you return your synopsis to Cornelius?

God, no. That would have upset him enormously. Who knows, it might be worth a fortune in a few years, when I'm old and grey and forgotten. It's in my case, I think, I can show it to you, if you want.

Did anyone else return theirs?

I don't think so. Brandon crumpled his up in a tough sort of way. He's obviously seen too many of his own films. Vladimir seemed to take ages to read his. Lucinda was sitting next to me, and she seemed quite upset with hers.

What happened next?

Well, the train pulled into Chargot, which is a longish stop to take on provisions and what-have-you, and the stop acted as punctuation in the conversation. Brandon saw his opportunity, and dragged his wife out. They started arguing the second they were in the corridor. Bit embarrassing really. I felt like a cigarette so I went out onto the platform for a smoke. Then I went to bed.

Where was your compartment?

Car A. I stayed there until I heard the shot.

You heard the shot?

Well, I heard all the glass breaking, which, when I heard Cornelius had been shot, I presumed it must have been the bullet. I got up and ran to the lounge in their car, where Maude and Vladimir were looking out of the window.

Had you seen Vladimir earlier, when you were on the platform?

No. It was only the railway johnnies rushing everywhere. I had a smoke with the waiter we'd had in the dining car that evening. Beautifully warm evening. Nothing smells and sounds quite like the Riviera in Summer with the salt in the air and the cicadas go........

Yes that may be true Mr Steels but what time did you go to bed?

Erm, probably just after half past eleven. I got undressed and sat in bed, writing a letter. I'd been there about twenty minutes, when I heard the glass breaking.

On your return to the lounge, did you see anyone?

Well, Mary-Beth Simpson was in her room with the door open, looking out of the window. Her husband's door was shut. Then I saw Maude and Vladimir in the lounge as I said.

So no sign of Lucinda?

Well, I...I did see her. I mean, it might not have been her. I saw her in the corridor, and then going into the toilet.

Which toilet?

There is only one in that car. The other is just a washroom. She was in a hurry. Almost running. As I said, I'm not certain it was her. It was dark, and I wasn't really concentrating. One doesn't like to point the finger in situations like this.

You sound as if this is a fairly commonplace event for you.

Not at all, but you know, a writer has to be a citizen of the world. Nothing should surprise a writer.

Richard Steels had a distinguished military record.
He regularly led near-suicidal attacks on enemy positions
but was discharged after rumours of his "unnecessary
barbarism" reached the top brass.

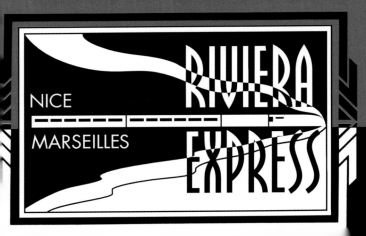

RIVIERA EXPRESS

NICE

MARSEILLES

Inspector Perciflage and Brandon Simpson.

How well acquainted were you with the deceased?

Aw, Cornelius was a great man, a very warm man, a very great talent, and I'm sure you'll join with me in mourning the loss of a very great writer.

But how well did you know him?

Well, my wife was very close to him. Don't get me wrong, all that stuff in the papers about them two, that's all lies, just malicious lies, and we're currently taking legal action against all the offending parties. There's gonna be more writs flying around than there were bullets at the OK Corral!

When did you actually meet him for the first time?

Only a couple of weeks back, but having read his books, and having heard all Mary-Beth's stories about him, I feel I've known the guy all my life. He talked my kinda language. I mean, primarily I was out visiting the little lady, but you know, any friend of hers...

So the purpose of your trip was purely recreational?

Exactly. I've been working so hard, picture after picture, and the studio have been begging me for months now to take a holiday. Marvin himself had to take me into his offices and beg me to kick back for a bit.

Marvin?

Yup! The Marvin Engels Jnr, head of RCP International, his very self! He said I was making too much money for them and the accountants were getting worried! So here I am in France, Europe, and I can tell you it's a pleasure. Apart from this unparalleled tragedy of course.

On the evening in question, what was your reaction to the summary of Cornelius' novel?

I thought it was real funny. He'd obviously spent a lot of time thinking up the jokes.

What did yours say?

Oh, it was just a bit of personal fun between Cornelius and me. Like an in-joke. You know, all the usual cracks about Hollywood guys being stupid and stuff. Made me laugh out loud. A lot of the others didn't find it so funny, I guess. You Europeans are real uptight.

So when you left the lounge, you were in a good mood?

Sure. I guess. I mean, I was real tired. See I'm not used to eating and drinking so late. And the French cooking, all those heavy sauces. Could sink a battleship. Me and the little lady had to finish packing, so we said our goodnights, and off we went. I packed and then read a book for a while.

In which compartment?

In my compartment. For your files, that's compartment number 1 in carriage D Inspector.

Do you and your wife normally sleep in separate rooms?

Excuse me?

Do you normally sleep in separate rooms?

I don't believe I'm hearing this. Look buddy, me and my wife earn plenty money, you understand, more than some bum of a detective like you. And in dollars, too. If we travel, we travel in style. It's as simple as that. You couldn't swing a cat in one of those crummy compartments. Look, I'll answer any questions about the murder, but you ain't gonna interfere with me and my personal business. Clear?

So you stayed in your compartment and didn't see anyone else. Correct?

Only Mary-Beth. I get kinda claustrophobic so she opened the partition between our compartments when she came to bed. That's the trouble with these old trains you know. They may be quaint but they sure are stuffy; none of the windows in our compartments, or in the lounge for that matter, would open - wouldn't budge an inch.

What time was that?

What time was what?

What time was it that your wife opened the partition?

About a quarter to midnight or so. We did the whole sweet dreams bit. Then ten minutes later, I hear glass breaking and then the whistle goes and the train starts moving. I asked Mary-Beth what she thought all the commotion was and she said maybe the glass breaking was just a waiter getting sloppy. She'd kept her door open and said she'd seen one go past seconds before.

You mentioned a commotion after the glass broke; what sort of commotion?

It's difficult to say cos I was half asleep. I was aware of people coming and going, maybe even someone running, in the corridor.

Did you stay in your room?

Yes. Yes, of course I did. Like I'm gonna get up and investigate every time someone walks along the corridor. But then I hear screaming, so I get up and go see what's happening. And there's Cornelius, with a hole in his head.

On the set of his "talkie" western "Devils Of The Delta", Brandon Simpson allegedly shot and wounded an extra who had twice fouled up an expensive long shot of a stampede. The studio hushed it up with a large cash payment. Four days later the extra was found beaten to death in an alley in Culver City.

Inspector Perciflage and
Mary-Beth Simpson.

You knew the deceased very well, didn't you?

In what way?

Well, erm, in the way that you were his biographer, and must have been quite...

Yes. Yes, of course. I'd been working with Cornelius for nearly six months, so we knew each other well. In a professional sense, I hasten to add.

Did he have any enemies?

Well, I'm not sure "enemies" is the right word, exactly. Like a lot of talented people, he quite often rode rough-shod over people's feelings. He was very focused about work, but he could easily slip into obsessive behaviour. He loved playing games when he wasn't working, and he took them just as seriously as his work.

Like the charade with the new novel outline?

Er, yes. Exactly so.

What did your summary contain?

Oh, you know, the same sort of things as the others.

"The others" seem to have received anything from mean-spirited ridicule to nigh-on blackmail. What did he have on you?

Nothing! It wasn't like that. It was just fun.

Your husband tore his up.

He hasn't got much of a sense of humour at the best of times, and he's under a lot of pressure at the moment.

What sort of pressure?

The studio is giving him all sorts of ultimatums, like if he doesn't secure a sure-fire script before Labor Day, then he's out. Stuff like that. Whether they mean it or not is another matter but he's taking it pretty seriously.

Did any of the assembled company have any reason for disliking Cornelius?

Enough to kill him you mean? I dunno. Richard Steels certainly had a chip on his shoulder about Cornelius stealing his ideas and his thunder. I think it's quite a common thing in literary circles. Steels likes to be a tough guy, always talking about fighting and shooting and so on.

Anyone else?

Well, that Lucinda is a little touched in the head. She's like a typically repressed, rich little English girl who's lived this really sheltered life in a library somewhere. Then she reads Cornelius' book, decides that it's changed her life, and then she attaches herself to him, like he's responsible for her or something. Or like she's got to tell him what to write about. Before this happened I told Brandon that I thought she was on a one-way trip to the bughouse, and since Cornelius' death, she's just fallen to pieces. Another weird one is Vladimir.

In what way?

I dunno. It's just sometimes he seems to be real smart, and other times he's real dumb.

Aren't we all a bit like that?

Sure, but I saw him having a row with Cornelius, the night before all this happened, and...it's difficult to explain, but they were arguing furiously, until they saw me. Well, Cornelius broke into his trademark smile, as you'd expect, but Vladimir just transformed. His whole appearance seemed to change.

What were they arguing about?

I imagine it was money.

Money?

They were both extremely enthusiastic gamblers. They spent most of the Summer in various casinos. The ironic thing was that Cornelius, the successful young novelist, was always completely in debt, while Vladimir, this penniless exiled aristocrat, was always there to bail him out.

So Cornelius owed him money?

I imagine so. He owed everyone money. Even me. God knows how much he owed Maude. Probably more than he made on the first book.

That's a lot of money.

But he was an artist. His writing was separate from the rewards that people heaped on him. He didn't write for profit you see.

And what about your husband?

What do you mean?

Did your husband have any argument with Cornelius?

No! No, he was just visiting me. He was on holiday.

People do argue on holiday you know. Particularly if their wives have been associated with other men in the gossip columns. Witnesses said that Brandon took you off after dinner.

We had to pack our things. We didn't argue and Brandon had no problem with Cornelius. Like I said, we had to pack.

What time did you return to the lounge?

After about ten minutes. My husband joined us at about half past ten. After that Vladimir came in. Then Cornelius gave out the resumés, and then we got into the station. It's a long stopover, to take on supplies and mail and so on. We went to bed soon after.

Did anyone leave before you?

No. I don't think so but I heard loads of people leaving soon after we did.

Did you see your husband after leaving the lounge?

Well, initially, for a couple of minutes, but then I had to go to the washroom, and after that I ended up going to chat with Maude for ten minutes or so, and then I went to bed. I said goodnight to my husband at about a quarter to twelve.

But you must have spent nearly half an hour in the washroom!

Inspector! Is this how you get your kicks, by asking probing questions about what women do in the washroom? I could easily spend three times that long in there!

After you'd gone to bed did you hear a shot?

I didn't think so. I heard people coming and going, which was what you'd expect, then I heard a crack followed by the sound of breaking glass. Then ten minutes later, when we're moving again, I hear these screams, and that was that.

Anything else unusual?

When I came back from the washroom, I did see Vladimir. He was hovering outside Maude's compartment. When he saw me, he made a big thing of straightening his tie, like he'd been looking at his reflection.

Which direction did he leave in?

The opposite to me, towards the back of the train.

What time was this?

When I'd finished..when I was leaving the washroom, just before I went back into the lounge.

Mary-Beth Simpson used to be known as Mary-Beth Lamarr. When super-successful showbiz impresario Gordon Lamarr left her for a budding starlet, Mary-Beth used her column to destroy his business prospects and his personal reputation. So vitriolic were these pieces that a rapid descent into alcoholism and drugs resulted in his suicide six weeks after the first mention in her column.

Inspector Perciflage and
Vladimir Kielov.

How did you meet the deceased?

Cornelius? We meet at party, big party, and then we meet at other party, and we meet in bar, and we become good companions, da?

I understand you and the deceased used to gamble together.

Casino? Yes, a little. I am very poor, because Bolsheviks take my money and my father's house, but I am clever in casino. Cornelius is very rich, so for him is fun. For me, no. For me, is the bread and butter. But he is good man. We are good friend. He invites me to his house, he gives me his hospitality.

Did you ever fall out with Mr Vernon?

Who is "fall out", please?

Did you ever argue with Mr Vernon?

No! I say he is my friend! He is my friend! Friend is not to argue. In my country, we are....

Did he owe you money?

What is "owe"?

Mr Kielov, you were given the option to wait another day and then have this interview with a Russian translator, but you chose to conduct the interview in English. Do you want to change your mind?

No. The English is fine.

If I think it necessary I can overrule your decision. This is an important interview. Now did Cornelius Vernon borrow money from you?

Yes, he borrow, but only little, and then he give me back. Also I live in his house, and I pay him nothing, so is like rent.

But when he died, he didn't owe you anything?

No. Maybe a little.

On the night of the murder, Cornelius gave everyone a piece of paper about his new novel.

Yes, I remember. But I don't understand it. I ask the young girl some question, you know, the vocabulary and the grammar, but she is silent.

Have you still got your piece of paper?

I think no. It is a very complicated evening. If you want, I can look.

How did the other people react when they read it?

Maude is almost crying, but she is from good family, like me, so she is just smiling, but I know she is very angry. The American man, he is furious, maybe with his wife, but why I don't know, Cornelius is the writer of it. His wife and the young girl, they are both like have seen the ghost, and Steels is, how you say when you laugh through the nose. Laughing, but a little angry.

Before everyone was given this paper, what happened?

After the dinner I go to find the cards for playing with, and a little vodka.

Did you do anything else while you were gone?

No.

But you were away for half an hour!

Half an hour? Really? I always get lost on these trains, they all look the same. I go the wrong way, I go to the carriage C, You know what it's like, da? Then, when I get back to the lounge in their compartment, nobody wants to play, and nobody wants to drinking the vodka.

What time was this?

About at a quarter to eleven. At eleven the train was arriving at Chargot.

After the pieces of paper were handed out, what happened?

Like I said, everyone was surprised. The conversation is dead. Then Maude ask me for vodka, and suddenly everyone wanting vodka.

So everyone had some vodka?

No. The yankees they go, he pulling her almost. After they leave, you can hear their voices. Cornelius is happy when he hears this. Nobody says anything. Maude is staring furiously at her husband, and drinking much vodka. Lucinda too. I never see her drink the alcohol before. The atmosphere is very bad. Why, I don't know.

Can you remember anything about the piece of paper Vernon gave you?

Yes, it was the story of his new book. It was about a Russian émigré, living in exile in Europe, I think.

What happened next?

Steels leaves to have a cigarette and soon after Cornelius he leaves, like he is bored now.

And then you left.

Yes. I remembered I had to send telegram.

At half past eleven in the evening?

Of course! The struggle of my people is not a sleeping thing.

What was the nature of your telegram?

I had to say I am in Marseilles, so in emergency they can contact me. Is very important.

When you went to the telegraph office, did you see anyone?

There were lots of guards and train employees on platform.

But you didn't see Steels or anyone you knew?

No, but is very busy. People everywhere. Also I am in hurry, big hurry, because I have important business.

What time did the telegram get sent?

I don't know. I lose the piece of paper they give me. Like I say, I was in big hurry.

When did you return to the train?

I don't know. But as soon as I walk into the lounge I hear the clock breaking, and there is much running, and so on. I am with Maude, looking out at all this.

Before the glass broke, did you see anyone walk along the corridor?

Waiter, maybe. I doesn't remember good.

So you were on the platform until just before all this happened?

Yes.

But you left the compartment just after Cornelius, which was at 11.20pm, so you took half an hour to send a telegram?

There were problems. Problems with the language, with the machine. These things take some time.

How long between the glass breaking and Maude discovering the body?

About five maybe ten minutes. Steels comes in in his night dress. Then Maude goes to Cornelius, and is crying very loud. Terrible. My friend is dead, my best friend here is dead, killed by some pig. A Bolshevik, probably. Terrible.

Vladimir Kielov starts crying if he is asked about what happened to his family. Even questions about where he grew up can send him into a state of profound melancholy.

Inspector Perciflage and
Lucinda Compton.

How long had you known Mr Vernon for?

I only met him in the flesh at the beginning of May, but we had been in correspondence for over a year.

Why did you initiate this correspondence?

Cornelius Vernon is...was the most talented, expressive and courageous novelist working in English, perhaps in any language, of the modern age. I nurse aspirations, aspirations which I'm sure seem merely fanciful to some, of becoming a writer, so what better nursery for a budding scribe than to drink from such a fountain of inspiration.

But hadn't he only written one book?

Two, actually. There was a volume of short stories, "The Flaming Muse". Inspector, do you know much of literature?

In my own language, a little. I have to admit I am unfamiliar with the work of Mr Vernon.

Well, put it this way. Richard Steels, who was heralded as a major voice of the immediate post-war period, managed to say far less with three novels written over a twelve year period than Cornelius managed to do in one novel written in under a year.

I understand you conducted a similar correspondence with Mr Steels, before moving onto Mr Vernon.

Look, it's no secret that a few poison pens in literary circles have described me as a "camp follower" and much worse, but I want to make it very clear that my relationship with Messrs Steels and Vernon was wholly platonic, and purely professional. I came to them to learn, nothing more.

So there was nothing in your relationship with Vernon that could have caused tension between him and anyone else in

the travelling party?

No. No. But people have imaginations, and some people have rather fetid and lascivious imaginations.

Do you have anyone in mind?

It's difficult to know where to start! It was such a strange atmosphere. I arrived at the villa in May, and there was already so much tension there. Mary-Beth was hanging off Cornelius, desperate to make her name from his. There was this creepy Russian hanging round, dragging Cornelius off on all-night drinking and gambling binges. And then Steels turns up, adding fuel to the flames. A paper paid him to write this article on someone who had effectively stolen all his limelight and reputation, and to this day I can't believe he accepted it. To me it would be like having to work for someone who had seduced my husband.

Did they argue a lot?

No. Steels was just really snide about everything, the novel, the fame, me even. And he did his best to eat and drink Cornelius out of house and home. And as if all that weren't enough, Brandon turns up, which really made things worse.

Because of the rumours concerning his wife?

A bit, I suppose. It was mainly his questions about Cornelius' new novel. Every meal would turn into this really purposeful interrogation about the subject, or the "story" as he kept on calling it, how many characters it had, where it was set. They were always really ignorant, stupid questions, and even though Cornelius had always said he wasn't revealing anything, Brandon would keep asking, so Cornelius would just pull his leg and make things up, but Brandon was so stupid that he'd believe it, and then get furious because it was always different to the last time.

And what happened when Maude appeared?

Oh, it got worse. Cornelius was just winding everyone up, flirting with Mary-Beth and me in front of her, then lavishing her with huge gestures of affection. Also, he seemed to have stopped working, but refused to tell anyone anything. And he was gambling more than ever. He was even asking people on the sly if he could borrow money from them for his nightly gambling excursions. Then he told us he'd tell us all about the book on the train to Marseilles. Then this happened.

You each were given a resumé.

You know about this?

Yes. What did yours say?

Oh, it was horrible. It was just mocking me, treating me like some idiotic young girl without a serious thought in her head, regurgitating all the "camp follower" allegations. Horrible. His work was brilliant, but he could be so cruel, so malicious. It was very spiteful.

Have you still got it?

No. No, I threw it away as soon as I could. It wasn't the sort of thing one would want to keep.

Were you in the lounge when the shot was fired?

No. I was in the washroom when I heard the bang.

When did you leave the lounge?

At about twenty to twelve. Everyone had left after they'd read their resumés, the Simpsons first. Brandon was furious. They went off to their compartment, and then Steels made his excuses and not long after Cornelius disappeared. Then Vladimir did the same, and I was left with Maude, who was distraught. She really opened up her heart to me.

What did she say?

How she'd obviously made a mistake about Cornelius. Either that or he'd changed completely in the time they'd been apart. She said he'd been unbelievably cruel to her, and that this resumé business had been the last straw, and that she could never forgive him. She was getting more and more worked up, and then Mary-Beth came back in, so I left. I couldn't face those two confronting each other.

So where did you go?

To the toilet. That's where I heard the gunshot.

Did you hear any other unusual sounds?

No. Just the gunshot.

And what did you do when you heard it?

Er...nothing. What was I supposed to do? I didn't know it was a gunshot. I...I just stayed there.

For how long?

I don't know. The guard blew the whistle and the train started moving. Then there was a lot of running around, and then some screaming. Then the train stopped and there was a knock at the door, and a gendarme told me what had happened. I was stunned. I was in shock...still am in shock. It was...nothing like this has ever happened to me before.

NICE

IVIERA EXPRES

MARSEILLES

An elegant, long, woman's evening glove was found by engineers in carriage D's plumbing system. Despite being extensively damaged by water and chemicals, it was still possible to see blood stains and scorch marks.

notes

Inspector Perciflage's Notes after the initial interviews.

Maude Malmaison Vernon:

Alone in lounge after Mary-Beth leaves and before Vladimir

returns. Lying about the resumé?

Richard Steels:

Clear motive, yet three carriages away in Car A. Keen to hint at

Lucinda being the killer

Brandon Simpson:

Rumours concerning wife and victim sufficient as motive? Under

pressure to secure hit script. History of violence and firearms

offences

Mary-Beth Simpson:

Motive? Lied about argument with husband. In washroom for half an

hour?

58

Vladimir Kielov:

Motive? BUT ability in English seems very changeable? Sent

telegram?

Lucinda Compton:

Motive? Claims to have heard the shot from washroom/toilet.

Which?

Access to resumés important to establish/clarify motive

Access to Cornelius' room - check if partition to Maude's

compartment? Access via open window?

Clock shattering? Bullet from murder weapon powerful enough to

be able to pass through victim and into the clock? Angle?

Glove - who did it belong to?

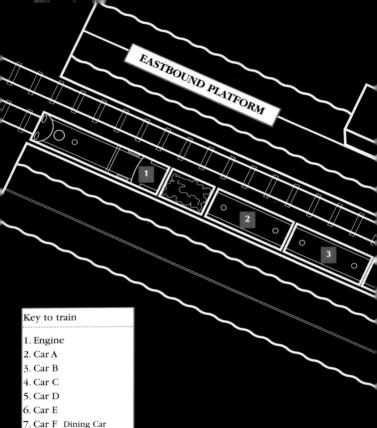

EASTBOUND PLATFORM

Key to train

1. Engine
2. Car A
3. Car B
4. Car C
5. Car D
6. Car E
7. Car F Dining Car
8. Car G Observation Car

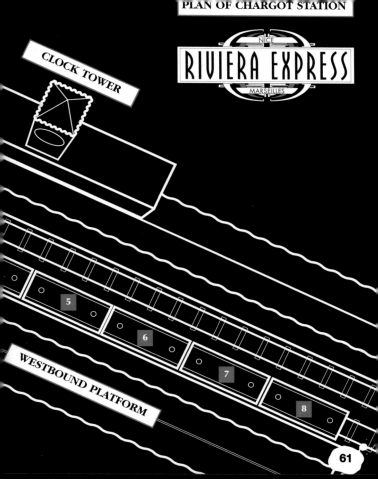

Lucinda Compton's mother disapproved of her daughter's foreign travels, fearing for 'her virtue'. As a precaution, she had given her a tiny .22 calibre 'lady's pistol'.

Chargot Coroner's Report

Date:	14th August 1935
Offence:	Murder
Victim (if known):	Cornelius Cecil Vernon, male, 34 years
Perpetrator:	Unknown
Location:	Wagon Lit D, Riviera Express, Chargot station

Analysis:

The victim was shot in the temple. On inspecting the body in the morgue, it became obvious that the entry wound was fractionally larger than one would expect from a bullet fired by the small calibre derringer recovered at the scene of the crime.

Analysis of bullet removed from victim's skull revealed it must have been fired from a 0.38 calibre weapon.

Further examination of the derringer confirmed that it had been fired on the night in question. No trace of the bullet was found. No clear fingerprints were discovered on the weapon.

Medical analysis:	Dr Jacques Zatapatique
Ballistic and firearm analysis:	Dr Pierre Lavisse
Officer on Scene:	Inspector Jacques Perciflage

When the train was inspected after the shooting, a policeman discovered a note pinned to the door of the observation car saying "Due to electrical failure, this carriage is closed for the duration of the journey. Many apologies. The chief steward." On questioning, neither the chief steward nor the guard knew anything about it and the electricity was working.

The steward said that the sign wasn't there prior to the stop at Chargot.

Inspector Perciflage

Here are the answers to your questions.

The records of the reservations you requested are as follows:

COMPTON, L
Car E, Compartment 1

KIELOV, V
Car E, Compartment 2

STEELS, R
Car A, Compartment 1

The cars are arranged in alphabetical order, with A situated directly behind the engine, through to Car G, the observation car.

All waiters stand down at half-past ten. Any further demands are dealt with by myself. I received no such calls on the night you enquired about.

Jean-Paul Beart

Jean-Paul Beart
Chief Steward

Maude Malmaison Vernon was wearing both of her evening gloves when the police boarded the Riviera Express at 00:35hrs.

MARITIME SERVICE OF THE FRENCH REPUBLIC
MARSEILLES DIVISION

21st August

In response to cross-service memo dated 19th August concerning retrieved firearms.

Three days ago a holiday-maker, Louis Saint-L'Eaux, a butcher from Chartres, discovered a pistol just below the low tide mark on the Plage D'Or, one kilometre west of central Marseilles.

Even though this is some seventy kilometres away from the murder site at Chargot, we pass on the information for two reasons. Firstly, the weapon is a .38 Webley, the same calibre as the profile in the memo. Secondly, corrosion and water damage is in concordance with the weapon having remained immersed for three or four days, which ties in with the eventual delayed arrival in Marseilles, of the Riviera Express on which the murder occurred.

Should the revolver prove to be the murder weapon, we shall expect credit for our officers who have responded to the cross-service call with typical Maritime Service efficiency.

Due respects

Jean Luc-Chagall

Jean Luc-Chagall, Duty Officer, Port of Marseilles

Inspector Perciflage and
Maude Malmaison Vernon.

I have reason to believe there were aspects of your story that weren't wholly accurate.

What do you mean? You still think I kill my husband?

Did I say that?

But I am suspect, no? Why would I want to do that?

Another witness told me that immediately before the shooting you said your husband was "incredibly cruel", and that you "could never forgive him."

I was very upset! And I was talking to this stupid, stupid English girl, who had been flirting and making the pass at my husband. Now she has told you this, and she has twisted it completely. Perfidious Albion!

You also lied to me about the resumé, didn't you?

(silence)

Didn't you?

It was only a joke, one of Cornelius' little jokes. A story about a writer surrounded by women throwing themselves at the feet, nothing special.

How did the story end? Did the writer leave his wife?

I don't remember.

Really?

I honestly don't remember! I don't know what the English girl has told you, she is just jealous. And as for the American slut, she is overjoyed now that Cornelius is dead. She treated him like a film star,

but couldn't understand his work, so now he's dead she's got the
best story she could hope for, with her being there for it all.

Do you have anything further to add?

I have a question for you Inspector. Did you find any jewellery in
my husband's possessions?

No, why do you ask?

Did you look in his briefcase? Perhaps you didn't find the key. He
always kept it locked.

*No, we found the key, but the case was empty, apart from
one or two personal letters and half a ream of paper.*

And the manuscript, of course.

We found no manuscript in the case.

Then we have been robbed! A string of pearls disappeared from my
compartment on the evening of the murder. I said nothing before
because I imagined Cornelius had taken them to get money for
casino, but someone has stolen the manuscript. You must search the
Americans, it must be them; he to make a film, her to get an
exclusive. Search their belongings immediately! That damned
manuscript is the only thing I have.

*We've kept all your husband's personal effects in perfect
order.*

I don't want a keepsake you fool! Cornelius has spent everything I
have. Without that damn book I am ruined. I have taken out loans
against it. If you police have lost it, I will sue you for every last
penny you have.

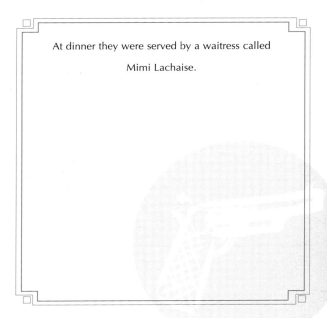

At dinner they were served by a waitress called

Mimi Lachaise.

HOLLYW
EATS   I
YOUN
A SATIRE O
IDIOTIC RISE
TALKING P

A story of criminally stupid Buck Dol
job on the line, he desperately tried
make his next imbecilic movi
realises his wife, Peggy-Su
passionate affair with th
better than anything she h
Buck sees a light at the end o
like a pact with the devil. If he ig
writer, he will be able to save his care
will provide a screenplay better than anyt
hadn't reckoned with the superior wit of
Buck's lack of perception causes him to
story changes, poor Buck swallows it whol
nothing; no script, no job, no wife. His wif
into the sunset with the handsome youn
fun at someone else's expense!

71

Inspector Perciflage and
Vladimir Kielov.

I feel obliged to tell you that the telegram office at Chargot was closed the entire time the train was there.

Oh. I...er...

And that you were seen outside Maude Vernon's compartment just after 11.30pm.

I was just...

And that Maude Vernon has complained about the theft of a pearl necklace. Do you have something to tell me?

Yes. Yes I do...is very long story. Cornelius, he spend much money in casino. Much much money. He always need more, so he borrow money from me. But I have not much money. I collect money for White Russian cause, da? Cornelius tell me to give him this money. I say no, is for brave soldiers of Mother Russia, so he threaten me to give him.

How did he threaten you?

He...he say he will tell Soviets where I am. So I give him money. Now there is no money, so he tells me to steal. He tell me his wife have this pearls. So I steal them. Then, when I am back with the others, he give us paper, and mine is story of Russian thief who rob beautiful French woman and is caught by French police, and given to Soviet authorities, who are shooting him. So I go to my room, I get the pearls and I try to put them back, but when I go, this Mary-Beth is coming out of compartment of Cornelius, so I have to go. I try later, and I hear a woman's voice in his compartment, so I cannot, in case is Maude and she come into hers.

Did it sound like Maude?

I didn't listen. I go back to my room to hide the pearls, then I go back to lounge. Then I hear glass breaking and the rest is as I tell you. But when I go to my room, after the police come, someone has been there. Is revolver on my bed.

You didn't think to report this?

Then you think I am killer. So I keep it, then put it in the sea at Marseilles.

I have to tell you we found a cartridge under your pillow. How do you explain that?

Is not me! Is not me! He was my friend. Why would I kill him?

ST. GERMAIN
INFIRMARIE

22 August 1935

Dear Sir,

We have a patient, a young English woman, who was found wandering the streets in an agitated and distressed state, unsure of her own identity, her location, and displaying classic symptoms of extreme shock. A search of her few belongings revealed that the patient is Lucinda Hermione Compton, and also a card with your name and details on. The Marseilles police have told us she is a suspect in an investigation you are conducting, and have posted a man outside her room.

Her disorientation is, I am certain, only temporary, and stems from some profoundly disturbing event or experience. She is currently under a programme of heavy sedation, and I expect her to be well on the way to recovery within 72 hours.

On the following page is a transcript taken from my notes and the observations of the nursing staff who have been attending to her since her admission. I have no pretensions toward your field of work, but I thought they might be of some relevance to your investigation.

BLVD. DE BERGERAC. 34 MARSEILLES

ST. GERMAIN
INFIRMARIE

The patient repeated the following phrases in a random pattern, over and over
again.

I never meant to, I was just trying to protect myself.

He was like an animal, hands everywhere, hands everywhere.

He lunged at me, and it just went off.

Bang-BANG! Bang-BANG! Bang-BANG!

Your initial reaction may be that these are simply the ramblings of a mad
woman, but extreme trauma sufferers indulging in this sort of repetitious
intonation are often reliving the core of their traumatic experience. As I said
before, the patient should be fit to interview within two or three days. I hope
this is of some use to you.

Yours sincerely

Dr Pascal Blier

Inspector Perciflage and Richard Steels.

In our last meeting, I feel you misled me about the nature of your relationship with Mr Vernon. Other witnesses have disagreed with the picture of good-natured rivalry that you painted.

Really? Well I suppose I did gloss over some things. One doesn't like to speak ill of the dead you know.

I've read Vernon's resumé. Did you really think he had plagiarised your work?

No, not really. I suppose my real gripe is that both our novels are about the experience of the Great War, an experience which he only picked up through reading books like mine.

Whereas you had lived it?

Exactly. It was more galling as a veteran than as a writer. Yes, I did resent his success, and I probably behaved quite churlishly at times. But at the end of the day, his actual writing is probably flashier and more modish than mine. Dammit, maybe he was just better than me. As you get older, I think it's easier to accept these things.

On the night of the murder, you said you saw Lucinda Compton, after you heard a shot. Can you describe what you saw?

She was in the corridor, and, as I think I said, she was in a hurry, going into the toilet. She was holding one of her gloves in her hand.

Did she acknowledge you?

No. I think she saw me, but she didn't acknowledge me. Did she say she saw me?

In which direction were you travelling?

From my carriage to their carriage, so towards the back of the train. I saw her from the doorway connecting C and D.

Earlier you said you had a cigarette on the platform with the waiter who served you at dinner. You were served by a waitress at dinner.

Did I say dinner? Sorry, meant luncheon. Pierre, his name is, from Perpignon. Ask him if you don't believe me. Talked about fishing, as I remember it. Or was it shooting? They'll shoot anything these Frenchies. And who can blame 'em, eh?

Anything else?

Oh, yes. I heard the American, Brandon or whatever, shouting, "Let's sort this out, here and now!" Didn't think much of it at the time. With some couples you get the impression they argue all the time. With hindsight, maybe he wasn't talking to his wife.

What time was this?

Oh, I don't know, before midnight sometime. About two or three minutes before the shots. Then I heard him storming around in his compartment.

But you didn't see him leave?

No. No, I didn't. Then everything was just as I told you. As far as I can remember.

THE FREE COUNCIL OF
IMPERIAL RUSSIA

Inspector Perciflage,

Thank you for your letter. I have to say that I was both confused and saddened by your enquiry concerning KIELOV, Vladimir. Vladimir used to be a close personal friend of mine, so I was surprised to hear that you are currently investigating him in relation to a murder. This surprise does not relate to the fact that the Kielov I knew was a fine upstanding individual, free from all the vices you mention. It comes instead from the fact that it was I who discovered his body in a Paris hotel room last year. He had been murdered. At the time we presumed he had been executed by Communist agents, a presumption borne out by the rapid reportage in the Soviet press of the "execution of imperialist Kielov" at the hands of "valiant international agents". The French police and diplomatic service

R/Vichy, 121 PARIS

wanted to keep the matter quiet, so it did not appear in the press here. It was reported in early editions of The Times (14.11.34), but was later withdrawn.

After the killing, your Parisian counterparts attempted to locate the hotel's concierge as a number of valuable personal items had disappeared from Vladimir's rooms between my discovery of the body and the arrival of the diplomatic service agents, but he had absconded, leaving no trace. They did establish that he was a dissolute Englishman, calling himself Robert Gough, who had worked there for five months. A while after the killing the diplomatic service agents said that there was a possibility that this Gough might have actually been Vladimir's assailant and a deep lying Communist operative, but after they failed to catch him, they retracted this speculation. They tell me the file is still open, but I feel sure they will do little more.

I know that there is a brisk underworld trade in identity papers and passports, but if the man in your charge is this Gough character, I would ask you to contact me, so I can notify the correct authorities.

Your loyal servant

Alexander Olgov

Alexander Olgov

Inspector Perciflage and
Mary-Beth Simpson.

I have a witness who saw you leaving Cornelius Vernon's compartment at around 11.35pm, at which time you told me you were in the washroom. How do you explain this?

I didn't tell you for Maude's sake. She was upset enough, without me making things worse.

Did she have reason to be upset?

About me and Cornelius? I guess so. Occasionally you meet someone who is just right for you, you know, there's a chemistry. You're French, you must understand that. We had something very special, which was cut short by this horrible event.

Did your husband know about this?

No, but I think he'd guessed. He was furious enough with Cornelius about the novel.

What interest did he have in the novel?

Brandon wasn't here to visit me! He's desperate, he's gotta get a script that hits as they say. He knows nothing about books, but he hears me going on about "this Vernon guy", as he calls him, he sees the sales figures, and he gets interested. Only Cornelius has already sold the rights to the first book to some two-bit English guy, on Maude's insistence. So Brandon comes out here to secure the rights to the second novel, and Cornelius plays cat-and-mouse with him for a couple of weeks. Brandon was near snapping point. It meant a lot to him.

So what happened?

Nothing.

Nothing?

Nothing. There was no novel.

No novel?

Nothing. Zilch. I guess Cornelius had spent too much time with me, and in the casino too. He lost interest in it.

Who else knew about this?

Brandon, cos I told him before I went to bed. I imagine Maude knew, too. It must've destroyed her. All that time, money and effort she put in.

How did Brandon react?

He was furious. Understandably. He wanted to sort it out with Cornelius straight away. I persuaded him to wait until the morning but of course he never got the chance.

Can you be sure of that?

Yeah. He carried on reading and I got ready for bed. I had just got under the covers when we heard the glass breaking.

Did you see anyone pass your compartment before this?

Well, only a waiter or waitress.

But you didn't recognise them?

No! If I couldn't tell if it was a man or a woman, it's hardly likely I'd recognise them, is it?

And you're sure no one else went past in the direction of the lounge?

Sure am. I saw a woman carrying what looked looked a white glove, run past the other way just after we heard the glass shatter, but no one else went towards the lounge, of that I'm sure.

Fragment of paper retrieved from train wastepaper bin.

QUEEN OF THE GUTTER

The new best-seller from the irresistible Cornelius Vernon.

Betty-Lou is a talentless, sleazy gossip columnist who becomes obsessed with dashing handsome young novelist Anthony Merton. What little imagination she has starts to work overtime, convinced that their relationship is something other than the temporary dalliance it so obviously is. She continues along this flight of fancy, descending into madne... husband expects her to use her charms to secur... for his next film. As a resu... no chance... all alone... penni...

RIVIERA

À VOTRE
SERVICE

EXPRESS

Inspector Perciflage and
Lucinda Compton.

The interview was conducted in the Infirmarie St-Germain and
Doctor Pascal Blier (the interviewee's doctor) was present
throughout.

(Dr Blier) I reserve the right to conclude the interview at any point,
and I must ask you to appreciate that the subject is in a very fragile
phase of recovery.

*Of course doctor. Lucinda, on the night in question, did you
go into Cornelius' room?*

Yes.

Why?

I was angry.

Why?

All Summer he told me I would see the new book. All Summer. Then
he gives us a resumé. But he just mocks me again.

What happened when you went in?

He...he said "I thought you'd come"...he thought...he thought I was
interested in him, you know...like that.

What happened next?

(silence)

He was all over me. Hands everywhere. Like an animal.

And then?

I just...I just meant to frighten him. I just wanted him to stop.

What happened?

Mummy's little gun. Mummy's teensy-weensy little gun. I just meant to frighten him. I just wanted him to stop.

Did the gun go off?

I just meant to frighten him. I just wanted him to stop.

Lucinda, did the gun go off?

I just meant to frighten him. I just wanted him to stop.

(Dr Blier) I don't think it would be wise to dwell on this part of the trauma any longer.

After you left, did you take off one of your gloves?

Yes. Just like Lady Macbeth. Just like Lady Macbeth.

And you went into the toilet?

Yes. Lady Macbeth in the toilet. I just meant to frighten him. I just wanted him to stop.

(Interview terminated due to extreme distress of interviewee.)

Only one bullet had been fired from the 0.38 calibre Webley revolver, found on the Plage D'Or 1km west of Marseilles on 18th August.

Inspector Perciflage's Notes.

Cornelius compartment - no connecting door to Maude's compartment. No one could have gained access via window without crossing busy railway tracks.

One bullet fired from derringer and one fired from murder weapon.

Webley was thrown into the sea by Vladimir. If murderer why wait until Marseilles?

If Vladimir is telling truth, who had access to his room between murder and his supposed discovery of the pistol?

Cornelius killed by only one bullet - therefore what happened to the other bullet?

Did anyone except Lucinda hear any actual shots or just breaking glass?

Significance of breaking clock glass: occurred at same time as killing?

If so, who does not have an alibi at that time?

CONCLUSION

This is the end of Inspector Perciflage's dossier.

The file contained all the necessary information to identify the murderer, as well as several red herrings and dead ends. It's now time to decide who the guilty party is but before you turn over to check the solution, think of your career. Early promotion to the rank of detective depends on your ability to crack this case.

Check through your notes carefully and compare them to those of your old friend, Jacques Perciflage.

(The first page of the solution is in mirror-writing, to stop an accidental glance ruining the book - hold the book up to a mirror when you turn the page, and all will be revealed!)

DON'T TURN THE PAGE-

unless you want to know the solution!

SOLUTION

Richard Steels was the killer.

His motive was jealousy. Vernon had not only stolen his ideas, his subject matter and his fame and reputation, he had also, in his eyes, belittled his war experience. All these factors were known to Steels before the night in question. What tipped him over the edge was the way Vernon freely admitted, even boasted about his plagiarism in the resumé. Steels had a history of brawling and fighting (the Momo incident) and he had also demonstrated an unhealthy appetite for violence during the war.

PROCESS OF DEDUCTION:

The 0.22 calibre derringer found at the scene of the crime was not the murder weapon. We know, from the Coroner's Report, that the bullet which killed Cornelius was fired from a heavier 0.38 calibre gun. The murder weapon must therefore have been the Webley found in the sea at Marseilles.

As only one shot was fired from the Webley then it must have been a bullet from Lucinda's derringer which hit the clock on the platform on the other side of the tracks.

The glass on the clock was heard shattering at 11.55pm. In Lucinda's final interview she admits she was in Cornelius' room, trying to push off his unwanted attentions (hers is the female voice Vladimir Kielov hears in Cornelius' room when he attempts to return Maude's pearls for the second time). She admits she fired her gun but only in warning and says she heard another bang straight after her gun went off. The second shot could not have come from her gun (only one shot was fired), so the murder must have taken place at 11.55pm or very soon thereafter, for the body was found at 00.05am.

So who had access to Cornelius' room around 11.55pm?

We can eliminate **Maude Malmaison Vernon** and **Vladimir Kielov** as suspects because they both said that they were together in the lounge when they heard the clock's glass shattering and we know that the murderer acted alone. Similarly we can discount **Mary-Beth** and **Brandon Simpson** because they too had each other as alibis. When Mary-Beth went to bed at 11.45pm, she had opened the sliding partition between their compartments.

Lucinda Compton was present at the scene of the crime for she went to Cornelius' room to try and persuade him to show her the manuscript, after leaving the lounge at 11.40pm.

Her reaction to the crime perhaps suggested she was the perpetrator, but the bullet that killed Cornelius Vernon didn't come from "Mummy's teensy-weensy little gun". It came from a heavier calibre weapon. Furthermore, after firing the derringer Lucinda runs into the toilet, where she remains until found by a gendarme.

Because of the location of the toilet, Lucinda could not have rushed into Car E and hidden the Webley on Vladimir's bed, nor could she have got rid of the towel in Maude's room, without being seen either by Mary-Beth or by someone in the lounge.

Richard Steels has no alibi, so he must have been the murderer. In the first interview he said he was in bed in his compartment from 11.30pm. But later in a second interview, he admitted to having heard Brandon shouting about "sorting this out, here and now" just before midnight. As Steels compartment was in Car A, he could not have overheard this unless he too was in Car D. Furthermore he talks about hearing "shots".

Earlier, in his first interview, he had nearly slipped up by saying he had actually heard a shot, rather than just the breaking glass. No one else, apart from Lucinda, heard a single shot, let alone two.

Not only had Richard been lying about going to bed, he had also lied about going onto the platform for a smoke. After he left the lounge at 11.15pm, he had not stepped outside the train; instead he had quickly slipped the anonymous note he had written into Cornelius' room and then gone down to Car G to stick the other note he had written on the door of the observation carriage. Aware of the interest both Mary-Beth and

Lucinda had shown Vernon, Steels hoped to lure Cornelius to the back of the train, where he planned to shoot him in the deserted observation carriage and then forge a suicide note. He then returned to his room where he changed into a waiter's uniform, which he had stolen so that he could pass unobtrusively along the darkened train, picked up the 0.38 Webley revolver, a towel to use as a silencer and his night-shirt. He then set off for the observation car.

On his way through Car D just before 11.55pm, he heard the commotion in Cornelius' room and, seizing the moment, shot Vernon a split second after Lucinda's derringer had harmlessly discharged itself through the open window into the station clock.

After firing a shot straight into Cornelius' temple (Steels was an ace shot; two of his favourite hobbies were hunting and shooting), he nipped round the corner into the washroom. While he was doing so, he saw Lucinda rush out of Cornelius' room and tear down the corridor to the toilet at the other end of the carriage.

Inside the washroom, Steels pulled the night-shirt he'd carried with him over his clothes (hence Maude noticing his trousers beneath his night-shirt) and threw the cabin-staff tunic out of the window of the now-moving train.

On passing the lounge in Car D, he had seen Vladimir talking to Maude and so ever opportunistic, he nipped into the next carriage, threw the gun on Vladimir's bed, and, as an extra precaution, hid the spent cartridge under the pillow, having wiped both clean.

Returning to the lounge, he realised he still had his makeshift towel silencer, which he tossed through the open door into the bin in Maude's room, before joining Maude and Vladimir in the lounge.

FURTHER INFORMATION

Maude Malmaison Vernon did not leave the lounge until she found her dead husband at 00.05am. The only time she was alone in the lounge was between 11.45pm, when Mary-Beth Simpson went to bed, and when Vladimir returned just before the glass shattered, so she could not have killed Cornelius.

"Vladimir Kielov" was really Robert Gough. Cornelius had by chance seen the crucial early edition of The Times and realised that his "collecting for the White Russian cause" was a scam. He promptly began using this to blackmail a share of Gough's ill-gotten gains to feed his gambling habit. Gough was neither murderer nor Soviet assassin, merely a petty thief and con-man who had seen a great opportunity to improve his lot. Frightened by what he had read in Cornelius' resumé, he had gone to his room when he left the lounge at 11.20pm and collected Maude's pearls, which he had stolen earlier in the evening when he went to collect vodka and playing cards from his room.
He planned to return the pearls but was unable to do so after seeing Mary-Beth leave Cornelius' room at 11.35pm. He tried to return them again later but was frightened off by a female voice, which he assumed belonged to Maude but was in fact Lucinda, at around 11.50pm. In the end he returned the pearls to his room and went back to the lounge, arriving seconds before the glass shattered.

Brandon Simpson returned to his compartment at 11.05pm and didn't leave it until after the dead body was found. Brandon told Inspector Perciflage that he and his wife did "the whole sweet dreams bit" at 11.45pm, but really Mary-Beth was telling

Brandon that there was no novel. Brandon, whose career depended upon securing the script, was furious with Cornelius and his little joke with the resumés and was overheard by Richard Steels shouting "Let's sort this out here and now". Mary-Beth explained that she managed to calm him down and confirmed that Brandon did not leave the compartment thereafter, for as she got ready for bed she could see Brandon reading his book.

They were together in their respective compartments, with the partition open, at the time of the murder because, as Brandon reveals, they had a conversation about the glass shattering and the ensuing commotion in the corridor of Car D.

Mary-Beth Simpson did go into Cornelius' compartment on the night of the murder but she had left it by 11.35pm when she went into the lounge to talk to Maude for ten minutes before retiring at 11.45pm. After returning to her compartment she remained there - as explained above.

Lucinda Compton was far too wrapped up in her struggle with Cornelius to see Steels but she did hear the minor sound of her gun and the more powerful yet muffled sound of Steels' weapon, hence her hospital chant.
She actually believes herself to be the (accidental) killer.
While inside the toilet, after firing the derringer, Lucinda flushed her glove, which was burned by the smoke from her rather ancient and dirty weapon and stained with Vernon's blood, down the toilet.

The waiter whom both Vladimir Kielov and Mary-Beth Simpson spotted going down the corridor of carriage D was Steels in his waiter guise, moments before the murder took place.